The Young Voyageur

by Dorothy and Thomas Hoobler
illustrated by Paul Bachem

McGraw-Hill School Division
New York Farmington

Pierre Montand woke up filled with excitement. Proudly, he put on the clothing that was the mark of a *voyageur*. On this warm morning in May of 1750, he was finally going on his first trip to Detroit.

Pierre's father and grandfather had also been voyageurs. Fur companies hired French voyageurs to take goods and supplies to far-off places and trade them for furs. The furs were then sold or traded for other goods.

Montreal, Canada, where Pierre lived, was the center of the fur trade in North America. At the docks along the St. Lawrence River, many furs were sold. From there, the furs were sent to Europe.

From the time he could walk, Pierre had paddled a canoe. Now that he was fourteen, he could paddle for hours without rest. Fortunately, he was not tall. In the canoes, long legs took up too much space.

Pierre's skills had earned him a place with a crew that was going to Detroit. Pierre would be a voyageur who managed the canoes and then returned to Montreal at the end of the season.

When the crew reached Detroit, he hoped to see his brother, Stephen. Stephen was a *winterer*, a voyageur who spent the winter in Detroit, traveling to Indian villages to trade for furs.

Pierre hugged his mother and walked to the river with his father. The canoes were being loaded. Men were busy spreading gum on the canoe bottoms to make them watertight. While his father talked with old friends, Pierre went to work.

The canoes were packed with flour and pork. They also carried goods such as blankets, beads, cloth, and knives to trade with the Indians for furs.

All of these things had been carefully packed into containers called *pièces*. Each pièce weighed around ninety pounds and had two flaps for lifting. With another voyageur, Pierre picked them up and laid them on poles at the bottom of the canoes.

At last, they were ready. The three canoes were lifted into the water. Pierre turned toward his father, who took him by the hand. "You make me proud," said Papa.

Pierre sat in the center of one canoe, the usual place for beginners. Opposite sat Jean, a friend of his father's and an old hand on these trips. The crew pushed off, and they all waved good-bye. Then Pierre watched carefully, dipping his own paddle into the water when Jean did. The canoes moved away from the shore. Just once, Pierre turned to see his father still standing there.

And now the voyage began! The cool spring air rushed against Pierre's face as the canoe made its way upstream. Each man had to keep perfect time paddling. They worked with great speed, about forty strokes per minute. Because he had practiced, Pierre was able to keep up.

To help keep time, the voyageurs sang. Their voices echoed through the forests. Pierre knew the words from his father and joined in.

For Pierre, the hardest part of the first day was keeping his legs still. That was a rule, for the gum that sealed the bottom of the canoe was thin. Anyone who shook it with his feet could cause a leak.

With relief, Pierre saw the lead canoe turn toward shore. It was time for a short rest. It felt so good just to be able to move his legs!

All too soon, they were on the water again. Now and then, Pierre saw a cross that marked a grave on the bank. The crew took off their hats as they passed. Many of those graves held friends. They were reminders of the dangers that voyageurs faced.

The day lasted longer than Pierre had expected. But he kept up his share of the paddling. Finally, the leader gave the signal to stop.

Before the canoe's bottom could touch sand, the voyageurs jumped out. Pierre helped unload the cargo. At night the canoes were turned over so that more gum could be spread on them.

Quickly, the men gathered wood for a fire and began cooking their supper. It was a stew of boiled corn with chunks of bacon. This food gave the name "pork eater" to the voyageurs.

Pierre had never been so hungry. He ate so fast that the others laughed. He spread his blanket and lay down. Listening to the men talk, he fell asleep.

Breakfast time came before dawn. “Soon we will come to the rapids,” Jean told Pierre. “They are too dangerous for canoes. We will have to *portage,* or get out of the water and carry everything.”

At the rapids, two men carried each canoe. The rest carried the trade goods. Jean helped Pierre put on a “portage collar.” This was a strip of leather that fit over his back. The other end was attached to one of the ninety-pound pièces.

Moving at a trot, the men carried their heavy burdens. Finally, the rapids were behind them, and they were in the canoes again.

As the days went by, Pierre felt himself become a part of the crew. The others joked with him. He knew that meant they thought he was doing his full share of the work.

A choppy stretch of water meant they were getting close to Lake Ontario. Now there were new problems to face. Lake Ontario was known for its sudden storms. During the storms, the canoes hugged the northern shore for safety from the winds and rain.

But there was another reason for staying close to the northern shore. The British had forts on the southern shore. Although France and Britain were at peace, they were rivals for control of the fur trade. The British had been known to fire on the French.

In good weather, they paddled all night. At last, Pierre saw the fort where they would stop. Here, the Niagara River emptied into Lake Huron. Down the river was Lake Erie. But they would have to travel overland to get there. The mighty waterfalls made canoe travel impossible.

At dawn, Pierre put on the portage collar again. As they walked, he heard the roar of the falls.

They slept before setting out on Lake Erie. By now, Pierre did not mind the all-night paddling. Detroit was at the western end of the lake!

Pierre heard a shout from the lead canoe. He looked up and saw the fort of Detroit in the distance. But why were the canoes headed for shore now? Then he understood, as they landed and began to change their clothing. They would arrive at Detroit as true voyageurs, men of style. Pierre put on his red cap, blue jacket, and colorful sash.

Then the three canoes raced up the river. Each was trying to be the first to reach Detroit. Jean smiled at Pierre as their canoe touched shore first.

Pierre was happy to be on solid ground again. He was no longer tired when he saw the scene before him.

The wooden wall of the fort was twelve feet high and two hundred feet around. Beyond the fort were four villages of the Huron, Miami, Ottawa, and Chippewa people.

Inside the fort, Pierre saw *coureurs du bois,* or runners of the forest. These Frenchmen were independent trappers who did not work for a company as the voyageurs did. However, both coureurs du bois and voyageurs worked and lived with the Indians.

All of a sudden, a rough-looking man took Pierre by the shoulders. And then Pierre recognized the man. It was his brother, Stephen!

Pierre had to help unload the canoes and take the trading goods inside the fort. That night, however, he ate with Stephen. The older brother described his long winter and his visits to Indian villages further west. He had traveled by dogsled and worn snowshoes the Indians had made.

For a month, Pierre's crew traded their goods with Indians who brought furs to the fort. The arrival of new canoes always brought Indians from far and wide. The Indians announced their arrival by firing their muskets. Pierre's father had told him about this tradition, so he wasn't scared.

The best part of their stay in Detroit was a large feast attended by the trappers and the Indians. Pierre and Stephen put on their good clothes. Heaping platters of meat and fish were laid out on huge tables.

Then it was time for dancing. The voyageurs whirled and stomped and showed off their acrobatic ability. Pierre danced until his shirt was glued to his chest with sweat. He would never forget that evening!

The voyageurs stayed in Detroit through June. Jean told Pierre, "It has been a good trip."

At dawn one day, Stephen came to say good-bye. He would be spending another winter in the Indian villages. "Tell Mama and Papa I will come home soon," he said. But Pierre wondered if he would.

Jean called to Pierre. They were ready to go. As Pierre leaped into the canoe, he felt a sense of pride and happiness. He had proven himself.

He did not know if he would want to live here all year like Stephen. But he knew the rivers and lakes would call him back. He had found his life's work.